YOU'RE SOMETHING SPECIAL, SNOOPY!

by Charles M. Schulz

Selected Cartoons from
The Unsinkable Charlie Brown, Vol. 2

A FAWCETT CREST BOOK

Fawcett Publications, Inc., Greenwich, Conn.

YOU'RE SOMETHING SPECIAL, SNOOPY!

This book, prepared especially for Fawcett Publications, Inc., comprises the second half of *THE UNSINKABLE CHARLIE BROWN*, and is reprinted by arrangement with Holt, Rinehart & Winston, Inc.

Printed in the United States of America
July 1972

I REFUSE TO CHASE A STICK THAT HASN'T BEEN PROPERLY SANDED AND POLISHED!

C'MON, FORGET ABOUT EATING! FIGHT LIKE A MAN!

NO! I'M NOT GONNA SHAKE HANDS!

IF YOU WANT TO GET OUT OF THIS FIGHT, YOU'RE GOING TO HAVE TO APOLOGIZE BY KISSING MY HAND!

SIGH

I ACCEPT YOUR APOLOGY!

SMACK!

WHAT'S A LITTLE PRIDE WHERE YOUR STOMACH IS CONCERNED?

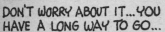

DO THUMBS EVER SPOIL?

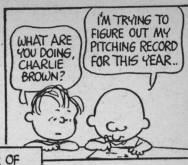

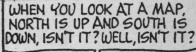

NOW, ALL YOU HAVE TO DO IS HOLD THE KITE LIKE THIS, AND THEN LET GO WHEN I TELL YOU TO...

ARE YOU READY?

FANTASTIC!

HAVE YOU EVER KNOWN ANYONE WHO HAS THE GIFT OF PROPHECY?

JUST MYSELF

YOU?!

ABSOLUTELY! I CAN PREDICT WHAT ANY ADULT WILL ANSWER WHEN HE OR SHE IS ASKED A CERTAIN QUESTION..

IF YOU GO UP TO AN ADULT, AND SAY, "HOW COME WE HAVE A MOTHER'S DAY AND A FATHER'S DAY, BUT WE DON'T HAVE A CHILDREN'S DAY?" THAT ADULT WILL ALWAYS ANSWER, "EVERY DAY IS CHILDREN'S DAY!"

IT DOESN'T MATTER WHAT ADULT YOU ASK... YOU WILL ALWAYS GET THE SAME ANSWER... IT IS AN ABSOLUTE CERTAINTY!

I'LL TRY IT OUT ON GRANDMA..

GRANDMA, HOW COME WE HAVE A MOTHER'S DAY AND A FATHER'S DAY, BUT WE DON'T HAVE A CHILDREN'S DAY?

EVERY DAY IS CHILDREN'S DAY

THE GIFT OF PROPHECY!

YOU DRAW A PICTURE AND I'LL DRAW A PICTURE...THEN YOU TAKE THE TWO PICTURES IN, AND SHOW THEM TO GRANDMA...

ASK HER WHICH PICTURE SHE THINKS IS THE BETTER..I PREDICT THAT SHE WILL LOOK AT THEM AND SAY,"WHY, I THINK THEY'RE BOTH VERY NICE"

GRANDMA, HERE ARE TWO PICTURES THAT LINUS AND I HAVE DRAWN..WHICH ONE DO YOU THINK IS THE BETTER?

WHY, I THINK THEY'RE BOTH VERY NICE

YOU JUST HAVE TO UNDERSTAND THE ADULT MIND!

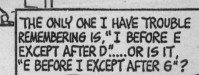

HELLO, SCHROEDER? GUESS WHAT... I CALLED TO TELL YOU I'VE BEEN LISTENING TO SOME BEETHOVEN MUSIC

I'VE ALSO BEEN READING HIS BIOGRAPHY...IT'S VERY INTERESTING.. SORT OF SAD, AND YET SORT OF INSPIRING...YOU KNOW WHAT I MEAN?

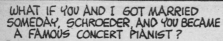

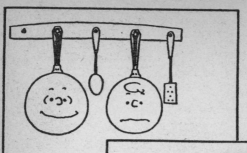

IF DECEMBER TWELFTH IS HERE, CAN BEETHOVEN'S BIRTHDAY BE FAR AWAY?

GUESS WHAT...BEETHOVEN'S BIRTHDAY IS THIS WEEK, ISN'T IT? WELL, I'M GOING TO BAKE A CAKE, AND HAVE EVERYONE OVER! HOW ABOUT THAT?

I THINK SUCH AN EFFORT ON MY PART DESERVES A REWARD, DON'T YOU? LIKE MAYBE A LITTLE KISS...

I MEAN, AFTER ALL, SOMEONE LIKE YOURSELF WHO ADMIRES BEETHOVEN SO MUCH SHOULD BE WILLING TO REWARD A PERSON WHO WORKS HARD TO...

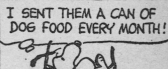

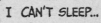

* SIGH *

I LIKE YOU, LINUS... I LIKE YOU, AND I ADMIRE YOU, BUT I COULD LIKE YOU EVEN MORE IF YOU'D GIVE UP THAT BLANKET...

I DON'T REALLY CARE IF YOU LIKE ME OR NOT...

HEY!

LOOK AT THAT, WILL YOU?

WHAT'S THE MATTER?

THAT BIG KID JUST PUSHED DOWN THAT LITTLE RED-HAIRED GIRL! WHAT A BULLY!

SHE GOT UP....BUT, LOOK! HE'S GOING TO PUSH HER DOWN AGAIN!

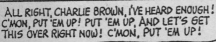